I am Kevin.

I am a puppy.

Wellington is my dad.

I run on the grass
with my dad.

I jump in the mud
with my dad.

I swim in the pond
with my dad.

Jelly has fun with
my dad and me.

I sit on my dad on the grass.

I sleep with my
dad in the kennel.

I am a hen.

I am in a hut.

I am a rat.

I ran in the hut.

The rat and the
hen in the hut.

Jelly ran in the hut.

Jelly and the
rat in the hut.

Jelly and the rat
in a net.